TROPICAL GEMSTONES

PERIPLUS NATURE GUIDES

TROPICAL GEMSTONES

Text by Carol Clark

PERIPLUS

EDITIONS

Published by Periplus Editions (HK) Ltd.

Publisher: Eric M. Oey
Design: Peter Ivey
Editor: Julia Henderson
Production: TC Su

Distributors
Indonesia
PT Wira Mandala Pustaka,
(Java Books - Indonesia),
Jalan Kelapa Gading Kirana,
Blok A14 No. 17,
Jakarta 14240

Singapore and Malaysia
Berkeley Books Pte. Ltd.,
5 Little Road #08-01, Singapore 536983

United States
Charles E. Tuttle Co., Inc.,
RRI Box 231-5, North Clarendon,
VT 05759-9700

Page 2: An Indian maharajah wears enormous diamonds
as part of his ceremonial finery. De Beers photo

Pages 4–5: Magnificent rubies and sapphires from Sri Lanka
Photo © Fred Ward 1997

Introduction

Asia is blessed with more gemological riches than any other region on Earth. The ancient diamond mines of India provided many of the most celebrated gemstones of all time. The earth and streams of Thailand, Vietnam and Cambodia yield rubies and sapphires, while the warm, clear seas of Indonesia and the Philippines nurture exquisite South Sea pearls. Myanmar and Sri Lanka hold the most dazzling treasure troves of all, producing gemstones of legendary beauty and amazing variety.

Most of the gem mining activity in Myanmar centers around the town of Mogok in the northern part of the country, which is nicknamed "Ruby Land." A mountain road from Mandalay, twisting through ancient teak forests infested with highwaymen, leads to this elusive land of million-dollar gems. In addition to ruby, Mogok and its environs possess large deposits of sapphire, diamond, spinel, peridot, apatite, scapolite, moonstone, zircon, garnet, tourmaline, iolite and amethyst. Upper Myanmar is the world's only major source of jadeite, the most beautiful and desired of the jade minerals, while gigantic South Sea pearls are cultivated in the tropical seas off Myanmar's southern coast. Top gem buyers from around the world gather in Yangon for the Gem, Jade and Pearl Emporium, an annual auction held by the government.

The tropical island of Sri Lanka (formerly Ceylon) is commonly known as the "island of gems" because of the spectacular range of jewels found in its gravelly soil. It is most famous for its lovely sapphires, but it also produces ruby, diamond, garnet, alexandrite, spinel, zircon, peridot, topaz, tourmaline, moonstone and a highly-prized chrysoberyl cat's eye. Gems are found throughout central and southern Sri Lanka, but large-scale mining is concentrated in the Ratnapura and Elahera areas. Sri Lankan gems are found in the crown jewels of Europe and in artifacts from China's Ming Dynasty tombs. Historians trace Sri Lanka's international gem trade back to 500 B.C., when Buddhists from northern India conquered the island and began setting its gems into jewelry for export.

Gemstones are deeply embedded in Asian cultures. In China, the cult of jade worship began in the Neolithic era, when objects made of the precious material were used in religious ceremonies, agriculture and war. Stone and Bronze Age gem mining tools have been uncovered in Mogok. Even the most ancient Sanskrit manuscripts are rich with tales of fantastic jewels, both mythical and real. Hindu literature tells of a jewel called Syamantaka, that hung around the neck of the Sun-god and gave him brilliance. When the Sun god presented the divine gem to a mortal, havoc ensued, as other mortals envied the owner. Syamantaka was a powerful gem which brought good to good and evil to evil, and caused the death of any impure person who dared to wear it.

The Kalpa Tree, a symbolic offering to the gods, is described by Hindu poets as having a trunk of diamond and roots of sapphire. Its topaz branches dripped with pearls and sprouted leaves of zircon. This magical tree bore ruby and emerald fruit.

One of the oldest known talismanic jewels is the Naoratna, or the "nine-gem" jewel. Old Hindu treatises list the nine sacred gems which make up the naoratna as ruby, diamond, pearl, coral, zircon, sapphire, topaz, chrysoberyl cat's eye and emerald. In modern times, the naoratna gems differ slightly—for instance, amethyst and garnet are sometimes substituted for zircon and cat's eye—but the spirit behind the jewel remains unchanged. Each of the gems are believed to be aligned with different planetary forces, and together they summon all the favorable influences of the celestial bodies. The purer the gems used in the naoratna, the greater the benefit it brings to its wearer. Poor or defective stones, on the other hand, can cause grave misfortune.

Enlightenment itself is described as a gem in the Buddhist faith—the rarest, most precious and beautiful of objects symbolizing the purest of human states. This belief is exemplified by Yangon's Shwedagon Pagoda, the most revered Buddhist shrine in Myanmar. A Myanmaran legend describes a shower of precious stones raining down on the site when the pagoda was first built, sometime around the 11th century. The shower of gems may be legend, but it is fact that the dome of the pagoda's stupa is paved with 8,688 solid gold slabs and its spire is encrusted with 5,448 diamonds and 2,317 pieces of ruby, sapphire and topaz. An enormous emerald is set at the tip of the spire, positioned to catch the first and last rays of the sun. Shwedagon Pagoda is known as "the gem of gems," and today is considered one of the wonders of the world.

European traders who made their way to Asia during the 17th century were astounded by the abundance of gems flashed by the rulers of the time. In the Great Mogul court of India, even the horses were decorated with precious stones. The famous French gem dealer Jean Baptiste Tavernier, who visited this luxurious court in 1638, wrote the following account of the legendary Peacock Throne:

> I counted about 108 pale rubies in collets about this throne, the least whereof weighed a hundred carats, but there are some that weighed two hundred. Emeralds I counted about 160 that weighed some threescore, some 30 carats. The under part of the canopy is all embroidered with pearls and diamonds. Upon the top stands a peacock, with his tail spread, consisting of sapphires and other stones. The body is of gold and a great ruby upon his breast at which hangs a pearl that weighs 50 carats. When the king sits himself on the throne there is a transparent jewel with a diamond appendant of 80 or 90 carats encompassed with rubies and emeralds so hung that it is always in his

eye. Upon each side of the throne are two parasols the handles covered with diamonds. This is the throne which Tamerlane began and Cha-Jehan finished. It is reported to have cost 160 millions of livres.

Behind this is a tub where the king bathes, the outside whereof shines all over with diamonds.

Today, many of the most fabulous stones from Asia's opulent past—including a few from the Peacock Throne—reside in the royal treasuries of Europe or in the permanent collections of the world's great museums.

In recent years, Asia has become even more prolific in its gem production as new sources have been discovered and new mines opened. Due to its skilled gem cutters and thriving jewelry-making industry, Thailand has become the undisputed center of the world's colored gemstone industry. Gems from Myanmar, Cambodia, Vietnam, Sri Lanka and India—as well as from distant lands such as Brazil, Columbia, Australia and Africa—pour into the Thai capital of Bangkok for processing. Everything from amethyst and citrine to the most priceless gems are cut and polished here, then set into jewelry ranging from inexpensive silver settings to elegant gold and platinum pieces encrusted with diamonds, rubies and sapphires.

Thailand is number one in the world in the export of colored gemstones and number two, behind Italy, in the export of finished jewelry. Together, gemstones and jewelry bring more than US$1.5 billion a year to the Thai economy, making it the country's third most important industry. A visitor to Bangkok cannot help but marvel at the brilliant displays of gold and flashing color in the city, from the gilded opulence of the Grand Palace to the dazzling diamond, ruby and sapphire jewels which fill the modern shop windows along Silom Road.

Gemstone processing and jewelry manufacturing takes place in India, Hong Kong, the Philippines and Malaysia as well. China is also beginning to get in on the act as its economy opens up to outside investors.

Not only do Asian artisans excel at making jewelry, they are also avid buyers of jewels. In recent years, Asia has become the world's most important market for jewelry with record prices set for pieces at Christie's and Sotheby's auctions in Hong Kong. Just as wealthy Europeans once vied to own fantastic gems engraved with the names of the Great Mogul rulers, today Asians clamor for jewels stamped with the imprint of such European names as Cartier, and Van Cleef and Arpels. The growing middle class, from Shanghai to Singapore, is well acquainted with the brand Tiffany.

Economic recessions, political turmoil and natural disasters may come and go but Asia's long love affair with gems is no doubt set to last for eternity.

— *Carol Clark*

Ruby

Asian origins:
Myanmar,
Sri Lanka, Thailand,
Cambodia, Vietnam,
India

Above:
A supervisor and
digger at a ruby mine
in Mogok, Myanmar

Photo by Carol Clark

Opposite top:
Rough and cut rubies

**Opposite
bottom left**:
Ruby from Myanmar,
cushion cut

**Opposite
bottom right**:
Ruby from Sri Lanka

*International Colored
Gemstone Association
(ICA) photos*

One of the most durable of gems—second in hardness only to diamond—the ruby is a crystalline form of aluminium oxide, infused with trace elements of chromium which gives the gemstone its red color. The name comes from the Latin word *ruber*, for red. Fine rubies are rarer than top-quality diamonds. They are also far more expensive, perhaps because red has always symbolized man's strongest passions, and no embodiment of red equals that of a first-rate ruby.

Today Myanmar is the most famous source of rubies. Nature embues the finest Myanmaran rubies with a red florescent glow, so that the stone scintillates with fiery life, like a translucent red-hot coal. Gem dealers call the color exhibited by Myanmaran stones "pigeon's-blood red," and large rubies bearing this description sell for millions of dollars. While Myanmar is the most well-known of Asia's ruby-producing countries, Sri Lanka, Cambodia and Thailand also have long traditions of ruby mining. Thailand's central location in the gem-rich region, combined with its relatively democratic government, have helped Thailand become the hub of the world's ruby trade. Most of the rubies from its neighbors pour into the country for processing and trading on the international market.

In 1992, rubies were discovered in northern Vietnam. The main deposits are in Nghe An Province, the poorest, most infertile region of the country, famous for producing tough soldiers and fiery revolutionaries—most notably Ho Chi Minh. Little did the long-suffering residents of the province suspect that their infertile soil held untold riches. When the valuable gems surfaced, they sparked a "ruby rush" in the province, even more fervored than the gold rushes of western U.S. lore. Thai gem dealers poured into Vietnam to pay cash for the rubies. Vietnamese subsistence farmers, used to earning less than US$100 a year, suddenly possessed valuable red stones which they could sell for thousands of dollars each.

The Nga Mauk Ruby

**Opposite top
left and right:**
Rubies from Thailand

Opposite bottom:
Rubies from Orissa,
India

ICA photos

The ruby is one of Asia's most revered gemstones. In India, it is known by the ancient Sanskrit names *ratnaraj*, "King of Gems," and *ratnanayaka*, "Leader of Gems." The Hindus believed that he who made offerings of rubies to the god Krishna would be reborn as a powerful king. The Myanmaran word for ruby—*ma naw ma ya*—means "desire-fulfilling stone." According to Myanmaran tradition, wearing rubies will make your wishes come true. The gems are also believed to give their wearers sexual appeal and protect them from danger.

One of the oldest sources of rubies is Mogok, in Myanmar. A legend attributes the founding of the town in AD 579 to a tribe of headhunters from nearby Molmeik. Throughout history the Mogok mines have produced rubies sought after by sultans, emperors and maharajahs. The Myanmaran kings, however, laid first claim to all significant stones of Mogok.

Failure by a miner to turn over a large ruby to the king brought dire consequences, as illustrated by the tale of Nga Mauk. This miner found a magnificent stone in 1661 which broke in half along a flaw—either by accident or design. Nga Mauk dutifully presented one 81-carat piece to the king but he could not resist the temptation of selling the other half privately. Shortly afterwards the king held a party at his palace in Mandalay. When he brought out the ruby to proudly show his guests, an Indian merchant said he possessed a stone of equal beauty and showed the king. Enraged, the king ordered Nga Mauk burned alive at a site now known as Laung Zin, or "fiery platform."

The Nga Mauk Ruby disappeared in 1885, when the British overthrew King Thibaw, the last king of Myanmar, and seized the palace in Mandalay. Some Myanmarans believe that the British took the stone and recut it for their crown jewels. Others, however, point out that the ruby could have just as easily been stolen by servants.

Sapphire

The sapphire is the serene, more subtly beautiful sister stone of the ruby. Both gems belong to the corundum mineral family and are essentially crystallized aluminum oxide. Red corundum—which consists of aluminum oxide and traces of chromium—is called ruby, while blue corundum—colored by traces of titanium and iron—is known as sapphire. Like rubies, sapphires are second in hardness only to diamonds.

Corundum containing other trace elements appears in a spectrum of colors, including yellow, violet, pink, green and orange. Any corundum gemstones which are not red or blue are called "fancy sapphire."

Blue is by far the most popular of the sapphire colors. The name derives from the Greek *sapphirus*, for blue. Since early times, the sapphire has been associated with celestial forces. In ancient Sanskrit it is referred to as *sauriratna*, "sacred to Saturn." Buddhists consider the sapphire a symbol for peace and faithfulness in love, making it a popular choice for an engagement ring gem.

Asian sources of sapphire include Myanmar, Thailand, Cambodia, Vietnam and Sri Lanka, which is known for its range of blue sapphire shades, from a delicate cornflower blue to a deep, royal blue. It has produced many of history's "celebrity" sapphires, including the 98.6-carat Bismark and the 423-carat Logan sapphires, both of which are part of the Smithsonian Institution's gem collection.

Kashmir, India is another famous source of sapphires. Tiny, needle-like inclusions known as rutile silk often soften and deepen the blue of Kashmir sapphires. Rutile silk sometimes enhances a sapphire's beauty by giving it a rich, velvety look, but if the stone is too lacking in brilliance, it is dismissed by gem traders as too "sleepy." While Kashmir has produced many legendary sapphires in the past, rebel fighting in the area has quenched its gem production in recent years.

Asian origins: India, Myanmar, Sri Lanka, Thailand, Cambodia, Vietnam

Above top: Sapphire from Myanmar

Above bottom: Sapphire from Kashmir

Opposite top: Rough fancy sapphires

Opposite bottom: Fancy sapphires, cut and polished

ICA photos

15

Enhancing Ruby and Sapphire

Below left and right: Yellow sapphires from Sri Lanka

ICA photos

It is estimated that ninety percent of the rubies and sapphires on the world market today undergo heat treatment, a permanent process widely accepted by the gem trade. Sapphires are so common in Sri Lanka that the palest, least valuable ones were once used in ornamental rock gardens or buried under the posts of village homes for a blessing. These low-quality sapphires, known as *gueda*, were not suitable for setting into jewelry. But in the 1970s, Thai gem dealers perfected a heat treatment process that transformed the worthless *gueda* into valuable gems. By "cooking" the stones at high temperatures, they worked a kind of alchemy. The titanium dissolved and mixed better with the iron, deepening the blue color of the *gueda*. The Thais then experimented on different colored sapphires and rubies, and learned that a valuable sapphire or ruby could be made even more valuable by "burning" out slight flaws. The process is risky, as certain stones may crack, melt or explode. In some cases, the gems lose all their color.

Star Ruby and Sapphire

Some rubies and sapphires have tiny needle-like inclusions known as rutile, or "silk," oriented along their crystal faces. When cut in a high-domed, cabochon shape they display a dancing, six-rayed white star. The star moves across the face of the stone with shifts in light, an effect known as "asterism." Fine star rubies and sapphires are highly valuable. The best ones possess an intensely rich body color and a strong, sharp star with all six rays equally straight and prominent. It is extremely rare to find a gem that combines these qualities.

Perhaps because of the blue background, which gives them a heavenly appearance, star sapphires were particularly prized in ancient times. They were considered a powerful talisman and a guiding star for travelers and seekers. The Sinhalese believe that a star sapphire protects the wearer from witchcraft. It is considered so powerful that even when the original owner passes the stone on to someone else he continues to receive its protection.

Below left:
Star sapphire

Below right:
Star ruby

ICA photos

Padparadscha

Asian origin:
Sri Lanka

ICA photo

The padparadscha is the most prized of the "fancy," non-blue sapphires. Padparadscha is a Sinhalese word derived from the Sanskrit *padmaraga*, meaning lotus flower, and was first applied to sapphires in 1847.

While lotus flowers occur in many colors, the original species is pinkish orange. A padparadscha sapphire is a delicate blend of these two colors. The effect is breathtaking—as magical as a tropical sunset. But unlike tropical sunsets, padparadscha sapphires are exceedingly rare. Some sellers may try to pass off a pink or orange sapphire as a padparadscha, but a true padparadscha calls for a harmonious blend of both colors, spread in a light, even tone throughout the stone. A stone may exhibit this perfect mix of color when viewed from above, but when viewed from the side, shows a distinct separation of the tones. Such a gem is simply a fancy sapphire and not the more valuable padparadscha. Many connoisseurs believe that a padparadscha sapphire can only come from Sri Lanka.

Spinel

Spinel is a brilliant red gem that is found in some of the same locales as ruby. This has led to great confusion in gemstone history, as spinels have often been mistaken for rubies. In fact, some of the famous "rubies" in the British crown jewels are actually spinels, including the 170-carat Black Prince's Ruby set into the British Imperial State Crown and the Timur Ruby—which is a 352-carat spinel engraved with the names of some of the mogul emperors who previously owned it. The source of both of these gems is believed to be Myanmar, where most significant spinels are mined. The Myanmarans recognized spinel as a separate gem species as early as 1587, but beyond its borders, spinel was referred to as "balas ruby" for hundreds of years. The name spinel is believed to come from the Greek word *spinos*, for spark. Spinel also occasionally occurs in pastel shades of pink and purple, as well as a pink tinged with orange that is highly sought after by collectors. Blue spinel is the rarest shade, and is known as cobalt spinel.

Asian origins:
Myanmar, Sri Lanka

ICA photo

Diamonds

Diamond is crystallized carbon, the hardest substance in nature. It has been associated with purity and fearlessness since ancient times and, more recently, with love.

India was an important source of diamonds for centuries. Until the 1700s, the mines of northern India were especially prolific. The island of Borneo, which today is divided between Malaysia and Indonesia, also had abundant diamond mines, from as early as about A.D. 600, although the stones were small, rarely more than one carat in weight.

The abundance of the Borneo diamonds before the turn of the century created a fetish for the gems among the Malay aristocracy and the Straits Chinese of Malaysia, Singapore and Indonesia. Wealthy women considered a stock of personal diamonds essential to their well-being. A mark of great status was having *berlian sama kachang puteh*—diamonds as numerous as peanuts.

Edmond Lin, in his book "Gilding the Phoenix: The Straits Chinese and their Jewellery," writes that one wealthy woman, determined to stand out in her bejewelled crowd, had her diamonds set into her teeth, in place of gold fillings. Society ladies of the time wore diamond encrusted brooches called *kerosang* to hold together their fashionable, buttonless jackets, known as *kebaya*. Each brooch was unique and custom made. According to Lin, after a matron chose a design, she might send a child or other relative with time on their hands to the jewelry shop, with a container of diamonds, to watch the jeweler work and ensure no substitutions were made.

While very few diamonds originate from Asia today, it has become an important world center for the cutting and polishing of diamonds from Africa, Australia, Russia and other parts of the world. India, Thailand and Hong Kong—and, increasingly, other parts of China—are known for the skilled workers at their diamond cutting factories.

Asian origins:
Malaysia, Indonesia, India, Myanmar, and Sri Lanka

Diamond cuts
Above:
Emerald cut

Opposite, clockwise from top left:
Oval, heart-shaped, pear-shaped, trilliant, square or princess cut and marquise

De Beers photos

20

Diamonds of India

Above:
The Idol's Eye

Opposite top:
Close up of rough
diamonds showing
their triangular
crystal growth

Opposite bottom:
While still in rough
form, diamonds are
sorted by size, shape
and color.

De Beers photos

No other diamonds have generated the mystique and supernatural power equal to that associated with the great diamonds of India's past. Diamond began its colorful history in India, where the gems have been mined and set into jewelry since at least 400 B.C. The diamond fields were scattered throughout the vast northern lands of Golconda, and the gems were traded in the capital city of the same name, which today exists as mere ruins near Hyderabad. Shah Jehan, the builder of the Taj Mahal, ruled Golconda during the period when many of the most remarkable diamonds were extracted.

It was the mines of Kollur in Golconda which produced the Koh-i-Noor (Mountain of Light) Diamond that today adorns the crown of Britain's Queen Mother. This diamond weighed 800 carats when found, sometime during the 14th century, and it eventually became the most coveted jewel of the Mogul Dynasty.

Indian legend held that whoever owned this diamond would rule the world. When the Persian Nadir Shah overran Delhi in 1739 he searched in vain for this prize. Indian folklore reveals that the defeated mogul cleverly hid the jewel in his turban. Nadir learned of this subterfuge and invited the mogul to a feast where he ordered him to exchange turbans. Nadir unwound the cloth until the diamond fell out. The sight of the gem so overwhelmed him that he cried, "Mountain of Light!"

The Koh-i-Noor eventually went to Lahore, the capital of the Punjab, which was later annexed by the East India Company. The diamond was presented to Queen Victoria and recut to 109 carats to enhance its brilliance. A superstition grew up around the diamond that it brings luck to women wearers and misfortune to men.

The Great Mogul, the Orloff, the Idol's Eye and the Hope Diamond are diamonds so rare and magnificent that it is impossible to assign a value to them. All reside in royal treasuries and museums.

The Hope Diamond

The Hope Diamond—the most infamous gemstone in history—came from the mines of Kollur, India. The French gem dealer Jean Baptiste Tavernier bought this magnificent blue diamond in its rough form of 112 carats during a trip to India in 1642. He sold it to Louis XIV, who had it cut into a drop shape weighing 67 carats. It was called the Tavernier Blue and was the pride of the French royal jewels. The diamond's large size and color makes it truly one of a kind—a deep, indigo blue radiating red, green, purple and black highlights.

Somehow the gem acquired an association with evil forces while at the French court. Apparently, a mistress of the king, Madame de Montespan, fell out of favor and was banished from the court after she wore it. Louis XIV later died of gangrene. The gem's reputation became much worse when Louis XVI and his wife Marie Antoinette were killed by their own subjects.

The diamond was stolen during the French Revolution and never appeared in the same form again. It is believed to have been cut into three smaller stones, one of which ended up in the shop of London jeweler Daniel Eliason. In 1830, Eliason sold this 45-carat, cushion-shaped blue diamond to British banker Lord Henry Philip Hope, and the diamond took on its present name.

French jeweler Pierre Cartier obtained the stone in 1911 from descendants of Hope, who blamed their bankruptcy on the gem, and passed the stone on to US mining heiress Evalyn Walsh McLean for $180,000. Fearful of the diamond's dark reputation, McLean had the gem blessed by a priest. But that apparently failed to remove its curse, since her son was hit by a car and died at the age of nine, her husband became an alcoholic and died in an insane asylum and her daughter committed suicide at age 25. New York diamond dealer Harry Winston acquired the stone after McLean's death and donated it to the Smithsonian Institution.

Topaz

The word topaz is believed to have come from the Sanskrit word *tapas* for fire, a reference to the range of flame-like colors of the gem, including orangey-yellow, amber gold and sherry red. It also occurs in browns, pinks, purples and blues. There is even an unusual bi-color topaz, combining blue and peach pastel tones.

The most valuable variety of topaz is called imperial topaz—a beautiful reddish-gold color—while good quality pink and peach topaz are also costly. The least expensive, and most common variety, is blue topaz. Most blue topaz is mined in China, where it actually comes out of the ground as colorless or white. Irradiation treatment transforms the gems into an electric blue. If not done properly, irradiation can make the gem radioactive.

While topaz is a hard and durable gem, it cleaves easily and care must be taken to prevent it from receiving a hard blow. An extreme, sudden change in temperature can also cause topaz to crack.

Peridot

Peridot is a lovely, bright green gem which is sometimes confused with emerald. In fact, before clear distinctions were made between gem varieties, all green stones were collectively known as *smaragdus*, which has evolved into the word emerald.

China mines large amounts of pale green peridot in small sizes of less than two carats. The low prices of Chinese peridot make it one of the most affordable of gems available in Asia. Traditionally, some of the largest, finest specimens of peridot have come from Myanmar, although Pakistan is now mining equally large and beautiful pieces. Gems in sizes of 30 to 50 carats can command high prices as collector stones.

Peridot occurs in fresh, bright greens and tends to be clearer than emerald, without a lot of inclusions. It is also much less expensive. About the only drawback to peridot is its relative softness. Special care should be taken to protect it from scratches.

Asian origins:
Myanmar, China

Above:
Peridot from
Myanmar

Below:
Rough peridot

ICA photos

Garnet

Asian origins:
Myanmar,
Sri Lanka

Above:
Rhodolite garnet

Below:
A suite of multi-colored garnets

ICA photos

Perhaps because of their blood-red color, garnets have long been associated with warriors, both as protective and destructive elements. The crusaders, for instance, decorated their armor with garnets as talismans to prevent harm. In latter-day Asia, garnets were sometimes used for bullets, in the belief that they would increase the severity of a wound.

Garnets occur in all colors but blue. Tsavorite is a vivid green grossular garnet. Red garnets come in several different shades, including a blackish-red, known as pyrope garnet, and a brownish-red called almandine. The most desirable of the red shades is that of rhodolite garnet, a vibrant, cranberry color with an affordability that belies its beauty and brilliance. The term "rhodolite" was first used in 1898, and came from the similarity of the garnet's color to the rhododendron flower.

Superior garnets are usually faceted, while the less valuable ones are often polished into beads.

Chrysoberyl Cat's Eye

Chrysoberyl cat's eye perfectly mimics the ghostly appearance of the eye of a cat caught in a pair of headlights at night. The stone comes in two colors: translucent honey brown or apple green, and is cut into high-domed cabochons. A silken-sheened slit of silvery white glides across the face of the dome whenever the gem is tilted slightly, widening and narrowing like the iris of a cat's eye. This eerie effect is caused by tiny, hair-like inclusions reflecting in the light and is known as chatoyancy. While this characteristic appears in other gems, none has the clarity and impact of cat's eyes in chrysoberyl.

The value of a chrysoberyl cat's eye is determined by the sharpness of the eye and the richness and luster of the stone's color. Some chrysoberyl cat's eyes exhibit what is known as a milk-and-honey effect. When a pen light is aimed at the side of the stone, one half will appear milky white, while the other half remains gold. Chrysoberyl cat's eye is a favorite stone for men's rings and cuff links.

Asian origins:
Sri Lanka, India

Above:
Pale green
chrysoberyl cat's eye

Bottom:
Honey-brown
chrysoberyl cat's eye

ICA photos

Tourmaline

Tourmaline is the chameleon gemstone, found in the widest range of colors, including black, white and everything in between. Magnificent tourmaline crystals can contain luminescent bands of several colors, from red to green to blue, just like a crystallized rainbow. It is no wonder that tourmaline is known as the "muse's stone" and is said to stimulate the imagination. Tourmaline is not only beautiful, it also has practical qualities since it becomes electrically polarized when heated.

Tourmaline is often mistaken for other gems, as it comes in shades of blue that mimic sapphires and can also appear as green as an emerald. The red and pink varieties of tourmaline are sometimes called "rubellite." The name tourmaline is believed to come from the Sinhalese word *turmali*, which means "mixed."

Although the gem has faded into relative obscurity in Asia, tourmaline was once much coveted in China. Members of the Mandarin class distinguished themselves by wearing large, round buttons of red tourmaline. The Chinese aristocracy also combined tourmaline with jade for use in jewelry. Empress Tzu Hsi brought the popularity of the gem to a head in turn-of-the-century China when she developed a passion for carved pieces of tourmaline. During her lifetime she bought more than a ton of the gems, including large shipments from mines in California. She had the crystals carved into utilitarian ornaments such as a pillow upon which she rested. Upon her death in 1912 and the collapse of the Manchu Dynasty, a rumor circulated that tourmaline caused bad luck. The market for the gem promptly crashed.

In recent years, the beauty of tourmaline has won a following among cutting-edge jewelry designers in the U.S. and Europe who have been inspired by the vivid colors and beautiful crystal shapes of the gem. Pink and green tourmaline is now widely available and especially popular. The gem is often cut into rectangular shapes following its naturally long and narrow crystal formations.

Asian origins:
Sri Lanka, Myanmar

Above top:
Blue-green
tourmaline

Above center:
Rubellite

Above bottom:
Bi-color tourmaline
crystal

Opposite top:
Rough tourmaline

Opposite bottom:
Tourmaline from
California

ICA photos

30

Emerald

Emerald belongs to the beryl mineral family. Traces of chromium give emerald its green color—the same element that gives ruby its fiery redness. Other beryl minerals include pale blue aquamarine, pink morganite, golden helidor and pale green beryl. Technically, light green beryl material cannot carry the title emerald—the color of a true emerald has been described as the rich, translucent green of new grass glistening after a rain.

The world center for emerald cutting, both in the past and today, is the Indian city of Jaipur. Emeralds from South America pour into Jaipur for processing and trading. Hundreds of thousands of Indian cutters facet the stones using the most ancient of techniques: a simple polishing wheel impregnated with diamond dust and hand-powered by sawing a bow string across the cog of the wheel.

Emeralds are considered one of the most difficult gemstones to cut. While they are extremely hard—harder than steel—they are also brittle and can easily crack or chip if not handled properly. They are also riddled with inclusions or microscopic impurities. It takes an expert eye to determine how the rough emerald should be oriented to maximize the beauty of its final appearance. They are most often fashioned in a rectangular step-cut, which suits the natural shape of the emerald crystal. This style is now known as the "emerald cut." Rather than bring out the sparkle of a stone, as in the case of the round "brilliant cut," the emerald cut focuses on the depth of the crystal, allowing you to appreciate the gem's color.

Emeralds characteristically have many tiny fissures and fractures as well as inclusions in their crystals. The French gave the poetic name *jardin*, or garden, to these inclusions, which resemble foliage. To improve the appearance of heavily-included gems, and to prevent them from cracking further, the practice of oiling emeralds developed. All sorts of oils are used, from mineral oil to special secret formulas created over several generations.

The Emerald in History

Above and
opposite top:
Two especially
inclusion-free,
translucent emeralds

Opposite bottom:
Trilliant-cut emeralds

ICA photos

Emerald is one of the most beloved of gems, with a colorful and long history, earning it the rank of "precious" stone, along with diamond, ruby and sapphire.

The ancient Egyptians discovered and cherished emeralds 2,000 years before the reign of Cleopatra. The rugged desert hills between the Nile and the Red Sea in upper Egypt yielded the first stones, at a site now known as Cleopatra's Mines. Another important early source of the gems was Columbia. The indigenous Indians of South America mined and treasured emeralds for centuries. The Columbian gems are typically more translucent and richer in color than those from ancient Egypt. When the Spanish arrived in South America, they immediately recognized the value of Columbian emeralds and began trading them around the world.

The biggest market was India. Evidently no source of emerald existed in India during ancient times, however the gem found its way there and became a favorite of royalty, including the Mogul ruler Shah Jehan. The insatiable appetite of Indian rulers for precious gems made India the center of the world's gem trade for thousands of years.

Emeralds enjoyed a special place in the pantheon of gem worshippers. The ancient Egyptians interpreted the green of emerald as a symbol for renewal, and would often use the stone to decorate the sarcophagus of a revered mummy. The restfulness of the emerald hue was believed to have restorative power for eyesight. In India, emeralds were also considered antidotes to poison.

To further boost their magical properties, words from holy scriptures were sometimes carved onto the face of large emerald crystals. Indian craftsmen perfected the art of emerald carving, creating lasting works of art such as the 217-carat Great Mogul Emerald, beautifully inscribed in 1695 with a Shiite prayer. The gem was sewn onto the garments or turban of Mogul emperor Aurangzeb for ceremonial occasions.

34

Moonstone

Asian origins:
Sri Lanka, India,
Myanmar

Opposite top:
Rainbow moonstone
from Orissa, India

Opposite bottom:
Blue-sheen moon-
stone from
Sri Lanka

ICA photos

This mysterious gem, captivating as a full moon gleaming in the night sky, is considered sacred in India, where it has appeared in jewelry for centuries. A mesmerizing interplay of light, known as schiller or adularescence, causes a silvery-white sheen to glide like veils of mist across the milky surface of the moonstone. Some believe that this moving light is evidence of a living spirit that dwells within the gem. Gemologists, however, attribute the shimmering phenomenon to the presence of albite crystals embedded in feldspar.

Indian lore holds that moonstone arouses the passion of lovers. If placed beneath the tongue when the moon is full, a moonstone is said to reveal what is in store, good or bad, for a romance.

The most sought-after moonstones have a haunting blue sheen, an effect produced by orthoclase feldspar, which is found almost exclusively in stones from Sri Lanka. Blue-sheen moonstones are increasingly scarce and expensive, especially since the main Sri Lankan deposit of the gems dried up in 1988. The top quality moonstones can cost $700 per carat or more. The largest and finest are often set into high-end jewelry, with the soft, lustrous gleam of the moonstone encircled by the brilliant sparkle of diamonds.

Much more affordable, and also beautiful, are the silvery-white moonstones. They are often fashioned into beads and make an excellent substitute for pearls.

Rainbow moonstones, which are actually a closely-related feldspar called labradorite, are also affordable. They come from a new mine in southern India and have only been in the gem market a few years. Their milky glow is flecked with lively sparks of red, orange, lavender, green and blue, which dance across the surface of the stone in an effect similar to opal. Rainbow moonstones are polished into cabochons or carved into artistic cameos for jewelry.

Zircon

Asian origins:
Cambodia, Vietnam,
Thailand, Sri Lanka,
Myanmar

Below:
Various cuts of
pale blue zircon, also
known as starlites

ICA photos

The zircon is a fiery gem that can be colorless, yellow, cognac brown, red, green or blue. The name is believed to have originated with the Persian word *zargoon*, which means "gold colored." The colorless variety of zircon has a brilliant sparkle and makes a convincing diamond substitute. Colorless zircons are sometimes mistakenly called Matura diamonds, after a place in Sri Lanka where they are mined. Pale blue zircons are sometimes called starlites, and the reddish-brown ones are known as hyacinths.

In ancient times zircon was believed to have curative powers and other mystic qualities. Zircons reached their peak in popularity during Victorian times when they were used extensively in brooches, pendants and pins. Today, however, zircons are commonly confused with cubic zirconia—the man-made diamond substitute—causing their popularity to wane. They are most appreciated by gem collectors who savor the variety of colors and the brilliance of this lovely, natural stone.

Opal

Opal is a hydrated amorphous silica that refracts light and reflects it in a play of colors. Australia is the world's main producer of opal, although much of it is processed and traded in Asia. The majority of light opal, the most common and least expensive variety, is cut and polished in factories in China, then set into mass-market jewelry for distribution throughout the world. Japan is the primary market for the much more expensive black opal.

Recently, Indonesia discovered several opal deposits on the island of Java. Only small quantities have been mined to date and most of it is set into souvenir jewelry sold within Indonesia.

The word "opalescence" was coined to describe opal's iridescent play of color. The stone comes in a vast range of patterns and vivid color combinations, making it the most dramatically varied of gemstones. One of the primary ingredients in opal is water, so care should be taken not to let it dry out or it could be susceptible to cracking.

Asian origin:
Indonesia

Above: Australian black and boulder opal

Below: An unusually large and fine Australian opal (50 carats)

ICA photos

39

Jade

The cult of jade goes back to Neolithic times in China, when the versatile stone was fashioned into tools and weapons, as well as symbolic objects for ritual. Eventually it came to be known as the "Stone of Heaven" and formed the bedrock of Chinese culture. China's religion, ceremonies, philosophy and art are all closely bound with jade.

The Chinese emperor drew his cosmic powers by holding a disc-shaped piece of jade called a *pi*. The pi was the most important of six ritual jade objects considered sacred by the Chinese.

Jade comes in two distinct varieties that are actually two different minerals: nephrite and jadeite. Both types of jade are extremely hard—tougher than granite and more difficult to carve than solid steel. Jadeite, although slightly harder than nephrite, fractures more easily.

The variety known as nephrite is a silicate of calcium and magnesium, while jadeite is a silicate of sodium and aluminium. Under a microscope, nephrite appears as tightly interwoven tufts of filament-like fibers. Jadeite shows a more crystalline structure.

Jade comes in a huge range of colors and patterns. White jade is usually nephrite. Blue-green, mauve, orange-red or lavender colors are most likely jadeite. Vivid, emerald-green colors—known as "Imperial Jade"—are always jadeite, and are the rarest and most valuable of the jade types.

Both jadeite and nephrite can occur in many other colors, such as brown-orange, red-brown, yellow-brown and black, as well as combinations of colors. The Chinese gave picturesque names to the many different patterns and hues of jade. "Moss in Snow" refers to a lichen-like, green-on-white pattern. The hundreds of subtly different white to yellow jades carry descriptions such as mutton-fat jade, chicken-bone jade, duck-bone jade, saffron jade and egg-yolk golden jade.

Jade in History

When diamonds were first introduced to China, sometime between 1005 and 221 B.C., they were valued more as jade-cutting tools than as quality gems.

Jade carvers in China held great status and their craftsmanship was astounding. They transformed this difficult to carve stone into the most delicate objets d'art, as well as practical and durable items. The royal courts abounded with things made of jade: cups, bowls and dishes, buttons, official seals, bangles, pendants, elaborate belt buckles with moving links, lanterns, hat stands, boxes, screens, garden seats, figurines of all kinds and even jade books with sheets of paper-thin nephrite inlaid with gold-leaf characters.

Confucius wrote that jade held all the most excellent qualities that men should aspire to. Jade is smooth and reflective, like benevolence; substantial and weighty, like intelligence; unyielding but not sharp or abrasive, like righteousness; lowly, like humility; resonant, producing a melodious note when struck, like music; able to incorporate both beauty and flaws, like loyalty; radiant, like good faith; bright and colorful, like heaven; of the hills and the streams, like earth; a fitting emblem of rank, like virtue; and esteemed by all who behold it, like truth.

Yu, the Chinese word for jade, took on a larger meaning and was used to describe greatness and beauty. A beautiful woman was known as a "jade woman" and the highest Taoist divinity was referred to as the "Jade Emperor."

Nephrite was the only type of jade used in ancient China, most of which was obtained from the Kunlun Mountains. While small deposits of jadeite exist in scattered parts of the globe, upper Myanmar is the only place in the world with a large and consistent supply of gem-quality jadeite. The Manchu emperor Ch'ien-lung quickly developed a passion for the vivid green Imperial Jade for which Myanmar is justly famous, and jadeite soon surpassed nephrite as the favored gem of China.

Jade and Buddhism

One of the most sacred of Thai relics is the Emerald Buddha, which is not emerald at all, but is believed to be made of nephrite jade. No one but the Thai monarch is allowed to get close to the sculpture. It is on view at Wat Phra Keo (literally the "Temple of the Holy Jewel Image"), which is adjacent to the Grand Palace in Bangkok. The Emerald Buddha is said to possess strong occult properties and is considered the talisman of the Thai monarchy, much as the jade *pi* symbol was for the Chinese emperors.

The Emerald Buddha's origins are shrouded in mystery. Exactly when or by whom it was carved is not known, however it first appeared in historical records in 15th-century Chiang Rai. Laotian invaders stole the image in the middle of the 16th century and transported it to their capital of Luang Prabang. It took the Thais more than 200 years to regain it after another battle.

General Chakri, who later became Rama I as the founder of the Chakri Dynasty, moved the Emerald Buddha to Bangkok and ordered two sets of royal robes made for it: one for the hot season and another for the rainy season. The current king of Thailand, Rama IX, continues the custom of personally changing the robes of the Emerald Buddha at the beginning of each season.

More recent times have seen the addition of another jade Buddha to Bangkok. It weighs seven tons and was carved from a single nephrite boulder. The towering image resides in its own temple and had its origins when a Thai monk received a vision instructing him to make the world's largest jade Buddha. He later dreamed that the massive boulder required would be found in British Columbia, which is now the world's biggest producer of nephrite jade. Informed that no jade boulder large enough for the project existed, the monk flew to Canada anyway, and a massive nephrite boulder was discovered by a Canadian miner one day later.

Pearls

Asian origins:
China, Philippines,
Indonesia, Thailand,
Vietnam, Myanmar

Above:
Pearls from Myanmar

Opposite:
Pearls are sorted by
size, color and shape.

*Andy Müller/
Golay Buchel photos*

Known as the "Queen of Gems," the pearl possesses a distinctly feminine charm and mystique. A pearl glows rather than sparkles, quietly but powerfully seductive, like the soft gleam of moonlight.

The pearl was probably the first gem to be universally appreciated by mankind for its beauty and rarity. Although natural pearls are extremely rare, they occur throughout the world, wherever oysters or mussels are found, in both salt and fresh water. Unlike crystalline gemstones, which usually must be cut and polished to be fully appreciated as ornaments, pearls need no help from the hand of man to bring out their allure.

According to an Indian legend, the Hindu god Krishna was the first to discover pearls, and was so entranced with them that he presented them to his daughter as a wedding gift.

The first written reference to pearls comes from China, where official royal records note that, in the year 2206 B.C., the king received pearls from the river Hwai as a tribute. The 11th-century Viet ruler Ly Nhat Ton reportedly paid an exorbitant sum for a pearl from Java that "glowed in the dark." On the other side of the globe, Native American Indians were using pearls to decorate sacred relics. When Christopher Columbus sailed down the coast, he bartered for as many of the New World pearls as he could find.

A famous anecdote about Cleopatra illustrates the enormous value that pearls held in her day. To impress Marc Antony with the extent of her wealth, the Egyptian queen boasted that she would serve him the most expensive banquet in history. During the banquet, she crushed a pearl from one of her earrings and dissolved it in her wine before drinking it down. She offered Marc Antony the matching pearl to drink, but he was too shocked to follow suit, as the rarity of fine pearls at that time made them worth a fortune.

The Pearling Industry

Known as the "Queen of Gems," the pearl possesses a distinctly feminine charm and mystique. A pearl glows rather than sparkles, quietly but powerfully seductive, like the soft gleam of moonlight.

The pearl was probably the first gem to be universally appreciated by mankind for its beauty and rarity. Although natural pearls are extremely rare, they occur throughout the world, wherever oysters or mussels are found, in both salt and fresh water. Unlike crystalline gemstones, which usually must be cut and polished to be fully appreciated as ornaments, pearls need no help from the hand of man to bring out their allure.

According to an Indian legend, the Hindu god Krishna was the first to discover pearls, and was so entranced with them that he presented them to his daughter as a wedding gift.

The first written reference to pearls comes from China, where official royal records note that, in the year 2206 B.C., the king received pearls from the river Hwai as a tribute. The 11th-century Viet ruler Ly Nhat Ton reportedly paid an exorbitant sum for a pearl from Java that "glowed in the dark." On the other side of the globe, Native American Indians were using pearls to decorate sacred relics. When Christopher Columbus sailed down the coast, he bartered for as many of the New World pearls as he could find.

A famous anecdote about Cleopatra illustrates the enormous value that pearls held in her day. To impress Marc Antony with the extent of her wealth, the Egyptian queen boasted that she would serve him the most expensive banquet in history. During the banquet, she crushed a pearl from one of her earrings and dissolved it in her wine before drinking it down. She offered Marc Antony the matching pearl to drink, but he was too shocked to follow suit, as the rarity of fine pearls at that time made them worth a fortune.

Above:
A strand of South
Sea pearls adorns a
bleached head of
coral

Opposite:
Each oyster species
produces a distinctive
shade of pearls.

*Andy Müller/
Golay Buchel photos*

South Sea Pearls

World War II interrupted the growth in Japan's pearl industry, but it recovered quickly after the war. The Japanese expanded their pearl production into the tropical waters of the South Seas, starting pearl farms in Tahiti, Indonesia, the Philippines and Australia.

One of their great successes was a farm in the Mergui Archipelago of Myanmar. The pearl expert Andy Müller writes in his book *Cultured Pearls* that the golden, lustrous pearls produced in Myanmar were an immediate hit when they first appeared on the international market in the 1950s, and for many years they were considered the world's finest. The quality of these pearls steadily declined, however, after the Japanese experts left the archipelago in the 1960s.

Today, South Sea pearls from Indonesia and Australia are generally believed to be the world's best. Australia is the top producer, followed by Indonesia and the Philippines. Other South Sea pearl operations are underway in Malaysia, Thailand and Vietnam.

South Sea pearls are impressively large, ranging in size from 9–17 mm in diameter, as compared to 2–9 mm for Akoyas. They also come in an amazing range of natural colors, from the famous black pearls of Tahiti to gold, cream, silvery, pink and blue shades found throughout the rest of the South Seas. In contrast, Akoya pearls are often bleached and then tinted artificially to achieve the desired colors. Not surprisingly, fine South Sea pearls generally cost a great deal more than Akoyas and are sometimes referred to as the "Queen of Pearls."

In recent years, China's freshwater pearl cultivation has made tremendous strides. The Chinese pearls come in a wide range of colors, shapes and sizes, are widely available and extremely affordable. The main wholesale market for the freshwater pearls is Zuzhou near Shanghai, but strands of Chinese pearls can be found in jewelry markets throughout Asia.

Quartz

Asian origins:
Myanmar, Sri Lanka,
India

Above:
Amethyst,
emerald cut

Opposite top:
Quartz of many
varieties

Opposite bottom:
Amethyst,
rough and cut

ICA photos

Quartz is the world's biggest mineral group, encompassing a spectrum of colors and patterns. This mineral occurs in two basic forms: crystalline and chalcedony. Crystalline quartz grows in a single crystal, while chalcedony is formed by millions of microcrystals.

Colorless crystalline quartz is known simply as rock crystal. In ancient times rock crystal was used to make crystal balls and it retains mystical associations to this day. Many people believe that wearing these crystals will enhance their health and spiritual well-being.

Amethyst is the most popular crystalline quartz for jewelry. Its purple color symbolizes celibacy and piety in both western and eastern cultures. Tibetans consider amethyst sacred to Buddha and fashion rosaries from amethyst beads. The name amethyst comes from a Greek word meaning "not drunk." The ancient Greeks made wine glasses from amethyst, in the belief that it prevented drunkenness. While amethyst is a highly affordable gem, large, top-quality pieces can command higher prices. Many fine amethysts reside in collections of royal jewels.

Golden-brown crystalline quartz is known as tiger's eye quartz and the greenish-yellow crystal is called cat's eye. Both of these types are usually cut into cabochons to display their chatoyancy effect—a ray of light that moves across the surface of the stone. They also make beautiful beads. Other varieties of crystalline quartz include citrine (yellow), rose quartz (pink), smoky quartz (brown) and aventurine (green). Chalcedony quartz includes agates and onyx, which are often carved into cameos or polished into beads. Fire agate has an iridescent shimmer like opal. Chrysoprase is a bright green chalcedony that resembles jadeite. It is used in carvings and cut into cabochons.

Jasper is an opaque form of chalcedony which sometimes grows in colored bands that give the stone the appearance of a desert landscape. Dark green jasper that is flecked with reddish-brown spots of iron oxide is known as bloodstone.

Unusual Gems

Above top:
Iolite
Asian origins:
Myanmar, India,
Sri Lanka

Above center:
Sphene
Asian origins:
Myanmar,
Sri Lanka

Above bottom:
Kornerupine
Asian origins:
Myanmar, Sri Lanka

Opposite top:
Kunzite
Asian origins:
Myanmar

Opposite bottom:
Dravite tourmaline
Asian origins:
Throughout Asia

ICA photos

In addition to producing many of the world's most popular gemstones, Asia offers a bounty of unusual and little-known gem minerals. New gem species are still being discovered. Iolite is a blue to purplish gemstone which closely resembles sapphire. Pale blue pieces of iolite are sometimes labeled "water sapphire," a highly misleading term since iolite is not from the same mineralogical family as sapphire.

Kunzite is found in Myanmar and comes in pale pink to lavender shades. The gem's color tends to be washed out except in the larger sizes of 10 carats or more. In Asia, large crystals of kunzite are sometimes carved into figurines. The brownish crystals of dravite tourmaline are ubiquitous in the region. While it is occasionally cut and polished into gems, dravite tourmaline has not caught on with the jewelry-buying public because of its undesirable color and lack of brilliance. Gem miners, however, love striking a vein of dravite tourmaline because it is considered a strong indicator that more valuable gemstones are nearby.

The yellowish and greenish-brown shades of sphene are more appealing because of the gem's luster and intense fire. Sphene gets its name from the Greek word *sphen*, for wedge, since the crystals are usually wedge-shaped. It is also sometimes called titanite because of its high titanium content. Sphene can make an attractive piece of jewelry, but it is soft and must be handled carefully to prevent breakage. It is found in Myanmar and Sri Lanka and is often confused with topaz or zircon.

Kornerupine is a favorite among collectors. Relatively rare, it occurs in Sri Lanka and Myanmar. This gem's most interesting characteristic is its strong pleochroism—a gemological effect which causes the crystal to appear in different colors when viewed from different angles. In the case of kornerupine, the colors range from green to yellow to reddish brown.

Indian Jewelry

In Asian cultures jewelry is often much more than mere adornment. It can be currency, a protective charm or an important symbol of status or rank.

India has probably the richest jewelry tradition in the world, going back 5,000 years and taking in the many different religious and tribal influences of this complex country. Throughout history, Indian women have made jewelry an essential part of their daily dress, sparkling and jangling from head to toe. Nose rings, earrings, heavy necklaces, arm bands, bangles, finger rings, silver belts, ankle bracelets and toe rings are typical jewelry accessories. If an Indian woman is too poor to afford the genuine article she will adorn herself with elaborate costume jewels.

The golden era for Indian jewelry was during the Mogul Dynasty—from the 16th to the 18th centuries—when the insatiable appetite of the rulers for elaborate adornment fueled the development of the jewelry arts. Enameling techniques and a distinctive method of diamond setting, known as *au jour*, remain hallmarks of Indian jewelry design today. The Mogul influence is clearly seen in lacy, multi-layered earrings and necklaces dripping with small diamonds, rubies, pearls, emeralds, sapphires and perhaps a few odd semi-precious stones. Color and quivering movement are important in Mogul-style jewelry, which would appear gaudy if not seen against the swirling backdrop of Indian culture, which seems to call for such excess.

Some ancient themes of Indian jewelry remain popular today due to their talismanic properties. For instance, a common motif for rings and bracelets is intertwined cobras, with rubies or diamonds set into their heads. These symbolize the *nagas*, the serpent gods of the netherworld. In Hindu mythology, the *nagas* guard the earth's mineral wealth, including gemstones. As jewelry, the snakes guard the wearers against harm and are said to be an effective antidote for poisons of all kinds.

Chinese Jewelry

The Chinese jewelry tradition relies heavily on jade. During the Qing Dynasty, it was trendy for women to wear jewelry made of translucent, green jadeite. Pendants carved into a curving dragon were popular, along with butterfly brooches, leaf-shaped earrings, cabochon rings and polished bangles. Go into a jewelry shop in any Chinese community today and you will see these same jade pieces. They are enduring not just because of their classic beauty, but because many Chinese continue to believe in the "good luck" power of jade.

In both India and China, where the worth of the local currency is subject to broad fluctuations and people have little faith in banks, 24-karat gold jewelry assumes a valuable role as an investment. In China, the world's largest gold-consuming nation, such jewelry is called *chuk kam* (pure gold). Workers will often take their year-end bonuses and head straight for the nearest gold shop, afraid to hang on to large amounts of the inflation-prone currency.

The *chuk kam* jewelry tradition is popular throughout Southeast Asia. The gold shops are usually family-owned and their patrons are long-term customers. The most important consideration is not the design of the jewelry but the amount of gold it contains. Customers buy when times are good, and when they need some money they simply take back their gold chains and bracelets and trade them in for cash.

In recent years, Asian consumers have developed more of a taste for gem-set gold jewelry of European design. This trend is fueled both by advertising campaigns from European brand name jewelers—such as Cartier and Bulgari—and also by the fact that such jewelry is increasingly produced in Asian factories.

Many young women in Singapore and Hong Kong are having the gems removed from traditional jewelry inherited from their mothers and grandmothers and having the jewels reset into more modern settings.

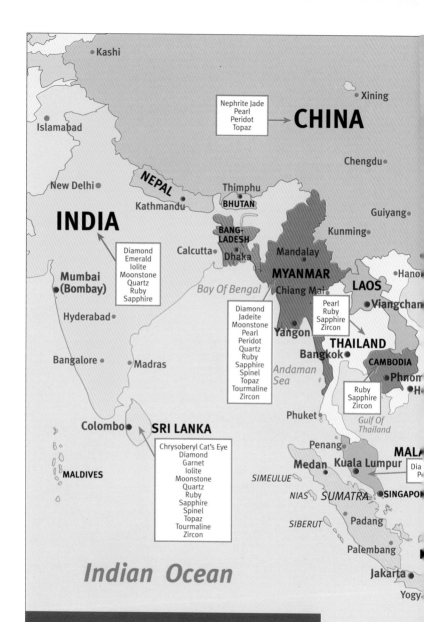

Kashi

CHINA
Nephrite Jade
Pearl
Peridot
Topaz

Xining

Chengdu

Islamabad

NEPAL

Thimphu

BHUTAN

Guiyang

New Delhi

Kathmandu

Kunming

INDIA

BANG-
LADESH

Mandalay

Hano

Calcutta

Dhaka

MYANMAR

LAOS

Mumbai
(Bombay)

Diamond
Emerald
Iolite
Moonstone
Quartz
Ruby
Sapphire

Bay Of Bengal

Chiang Mai

Viangchan

Hyderabad

Diamond
Jadeite
Moonstone
Pearl
Peridot
Quartz
Ruby
Sapphire
Spinel
Topaz
Tourmaline
Zircon

Pearl
Ruby
Sapphire
Zircon

Bangalore

Madras

Yangon

THAILAND

Bangkok

CAMBODIA

Phnom

Andaman
Sea

Ruby
Sapphire
Zircon

H

Colombo

SRI LANKA

Phuket

Gulf Of
Thailand

Penang

Chrysoberyl Cat's Eye
Diamond
Garnet
Iolite
Moonstone
Quartz
Ruby
Sapphire
Spinel
Topaz
Tourmaline
Zircon

MALDIVES

Medan

Kuala Lumpur

MALA

Dia
P

SIMEULUE

NIAS

SUMATRA

SINGAPO

SIBERUT

Padang

Palembang

Indian Ocean

Jakarta

Yogy

GEMSTONES IN ASIA

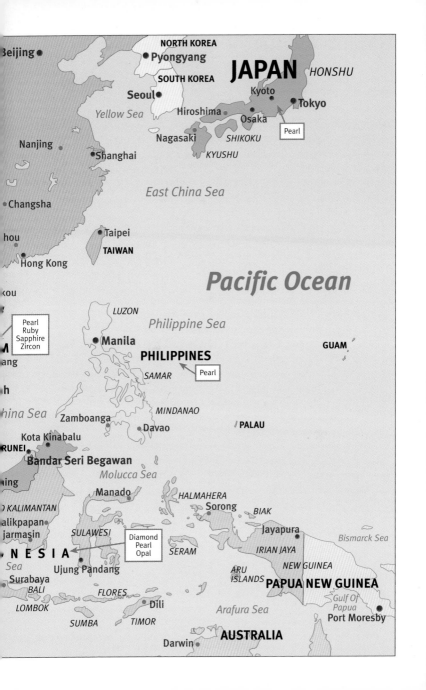

Buying Gemstones

Asia has a huge variety of gemstones to offer, in a wide range of quality and prices, making it a tempting place to buy—even for those who are not jewelry fanatics. The region's bustling gem districts and modern jewelry stores can offer good value. However, a few words of caution are in order.

The International Colored Gemstone Association (ICA) points out that most of the problems consumers have with gemstone and jewelry purchases are the result of trying to get something for less than it is worth. No matter how much you want to believe it, the average consumer will never get the best of a professional gem trader, even if that gem trader appears naive and friendly. Tourists are especially vulnerable to the illusion that the friendlier the people, and the more primitive the setting, the better the deal they will get. The opposite is usually true in regard to gemstones. A good rule of thumb is that the closer you get to a gemstone mine site, the greater the number of synthetics in the marketplace. Leave the border town deals in smoky back rooms to the experts.

Also avoid buying gems from the street. The ICA puts it this way: "Would you buy on the street in New York City? Buying on the street in Rangoon will probably have the same result." The key is to buy from a reputable shop. There are many such shops in Asia, although the tourist sometimes has difficulty finding them, because touts and tour operators are often determined to lead them astray, in the hopes of earning a commission. Common scams involve telling purchasers stories such as: "A special government tax is being waived for gemstone purchases and today is the last day."

Other red flags to watch out for are shops that claim they are giving you a wholesale price (why would they do that?) or that you can resell your purchase when you return to your home country for double or triple what you paid. Walk out of a jewelry shop that makes such claims or uses any high-pressure sales tactics that make you feel uncomfortable. Also, remember that certificates or written guarantees do not necessarily hold water.

Once you have it firmly in mind that your goal is not to get something for less than it is worth, but to buy a quality gem that you can appreciate and enjoy for years, you are no longer an easy target for rip-offs. Patronize jewelry shops staffed by people who are willing to show you a wide selection of the types and qualities of gems available in Asia, and can answer all of your questions satisfactorily. Visit several such jewelry stores and compare prices before you make a purchase.

Evaluate gemstones using the four "Cs": carat weight, color, clarity and cut.

One carat equals one-fifth of a gram, the unit of measure by which gemstones are sold. Generally, the heavier the gem, the higher the price. From the consumer's standpoint, much of that weight should be showing on the face of the stone, or the table. This is where the cut of the gem comes into play. If the gem is cut too deep, most of the carat weight is hidden from the eye and the color may be too dark. A gem cut too shallow, on the other hand, will lack brilliance and have a flat, washed-out look. An ideally cut gem reflects light evenly from all parts of the table.

Trust your own eyes when judging the color of a gem. When shopping for rubies, for instance, ask to see a range of colors and qualities available. You will be surprised at the variation in ruby shades, with the reds often showing hints of pink, orange or purple. It is mostly a matter of personal taste as to which shade is the best. No matter what the shade, the brighter, richer and more vivid the color, the more valuable the stone. Look at the gems in different lights. Some gems look magnificent under florescent lights but appear lifeless in daylight, or vice versa.

Clarity is another important consideration. Only glass or gems of phenomenal value have no inclusions visible to the eye. Flaws can add interest, but look for those jewels with flaws that are least obvious when the gem is viewed face up. Emeralds have more inclusions and small fractures than most other gems. While you cannot avoid internal inclusions in emeralds, avoid those with cracks that reach the surface, as they could affect the durability of the gem.

Pearls also come in a variety of sizes, shapes and shades. Freshwater pearls are the least expensive, sometimes selling for less than costume jewelry. Cultured Akoya pearls are more expensive, but still affordable, while fine South Sea pearls represent a major investment for most people. Your budget will most likely determine which type of pearls you choose. As for color, trust your own eyes and select the shade most pleasing to you and complementary to your skin tone.

A rich luster is more important than color when determining the value of a pearl. The surface should give an illusion of great depth, as though you were looking into a crystalline pool of water reflecting a cloudy sky. While some tiny spots and impurities are inevitable on the surface, they do not necessarily detract from the beauty of a pearl. Also, a perfectly round shape is not essential. An imaginative designer can transform a baroque-shaped pearl into a stunning and utterly unique piece of jewelry.

Index

Agate 52

Akoya pearls 48, 63

Alexandrite 7

Amethyst 7, 8,9,52–53

Apatite 7

Aventurine 52

Balas ruby 19

Bloodstone 52

Buying Gemstones 62–63

Chalcedony quartz 52

Chrysoberyl cat's eye 7, 8, 29

Chrysoprase 52

Citrine 52

Cubic zirconia 38

Cultured pearls 48–51

Diamonds 7, 8, 9, 20–25, 56–57

Dravite tourmaline 54–55

Emerald 8, 9, 27, 32–35, 56, 63

Freshwater pearls 50, 63

Garnet 7, 8, 28

Great Mogul Emerald 34

Hope Diamond 24

Idol's Eye 22

Iolite 7, 54

Jade 30, 40–45, 58–59

Jade and Buddhism 44

Jadeite 40, 58–59

Jasper 52

Jewelry 9, 20, 56–59

   Indian 56

   Chinese 58, 59

Kornerupine 54

Kunzite 54–55

Labradorite 36

Map 60–61

Matura diamonds 38

Moonstone 7, 36–37

Mountain of Light Diamond 22

Nephrite 40, 42, 44–45

Onyx 52

Opal 39

Padparadscha 18

Pearls 7, 8, 46–51, 56, 63

Peridot 7, 27

Quartz 52–53

Rock crystal 52–53

Rose quartz 52

Ruby 4–5, 7, 8, 9, 10–13, 16, 17, 19, 56, 63

Sapphire 4–5, 7, 8, 9, 14–15, 16, 17, 18, 56–57

Scapolite 7

Smoky quartz 52

South Sea pearls 50–51

Sphene 54

Spinel 7, 19

Tiger's eye quartz 52

Topaz 7, 8, 26

Tourmaline 7, 30–31, 54–55

Unusual Gems 54–55

Zircon 7, 8, 38